JUST ME AND MY BICYCLE

BY GINA AND MERCER MAYER

Reader's Digest Kids

Westport, Connecticut

I have a really cool bicycle.
It's shiny and red and almost
as big as me.

Dad said, "You have to take
good care of a nice bicycle like this."
I said I would.

So I always keep it clean and shiny—
well, almost always.

And I put it in the garage every night.
If I forget, I have to go out in the dark
to put it away. That helps me remember.

My bike takes me everywhere
I want to go. As long as it's not
across the street.

My bike and I have lots of adventures
together.
When I'm a spy, we hide in the bushes
gathering top secret information.
Then we ride at top speed to our
headquarters. We never get caught.

When I'm a policeman, my bike is my motorcycle. We speed around chasing bad guys. We always catch them.

When I am a cowboy, my bike is
my bucking bronco. But it never
throws me off.

Today my friends came over to my house.
We played on our bikes. We made a
bridge over the ditch in the backyard.
We had a lot of fun riding over it.
Until it broke.

Then we took turns pulling each other
in the wagon. Mom made us stop
because we might get hurt.

After my friends went home,
I asked Mom and Dad to go
on a bike ride with me.

My sister sat in a special seat on Mom's bike. She doesn't have a big bike because her legs are too short to reach the pedals.

We rode all over town. We even rode
across the street. Mom and Dad
got tired, but I didn't.

Then we stopped and had an ice cream cone.
I wanted to ride my bike while I ate my cone,
but Mom said, "Sit down."

On the way home I hit a big bump.
I fell off my bike and hurt my knee.
It started bleeding. That made me cry.

Dad gave me a hug and said
it would be okay. He wanted me
to get back on my bike.

I said no. I was mad at my bike for making me fall. I even kicked it. Mom said, "It's not the bike's fault you fell. It was just an accident."

I wasn't so sure, but I got back on my bike
and we rode home. I didn't fall anymore.
I guess Mom was right.

When we got home, my sister wanted to ride my bike. My dad sat her on it and pushed her around the driveway. Then my dad went to buy helmets for the whole family—just in case.

When my sister's legs get longer, maybe she will have a big bike, too. Then I can show her how to take care of it.

She might even be lucky enough
to get a bike as good as mine—
well, almost as good.